DRAWING ATTENTION

INK SPLATS & INSPIRATION FROM

BANDEIRA

THE YORKSHIRE POST

GREAT N ORTHERN

Great Northern Books Limited
PO Box 1380, Bradford, BD5 5FB
www.greatnorthernbooks.co.uk

ISBN: 978-1-912101-89-4

Layout: David Burrill

CIP Data
A catalogue for this book is available
from the British Library

Printed and bound in India

I'd like to dedicate this book to my late Mam who passed away February 2017 after a long battle with mental illness. I produced the first cartoon two weeks after her death and she is the one person who inspired me to complete this project with every ounce of expression possible. Without her support, encouragement and dedication to my work, this book wouldn't have happened.

When I was at the height of my playing career, Roy Ullyett, Matt, Mac and JAK were all well known and depicted me in their cartoons.

Nowadays it is the turn of Joe Root because he is a star and one of the top three batsmen in World cricket along with Virat Kohli and Steve Smith.

Graeme has the same ability with his talent to take topical events and somehow bring them to life in an amusing way.

I wish him well with his book.

Thanks,

Geoffrey Boycott

The art of editing really isn't an art at all. I sum it up thus: identify your most talented people and, first and foremost, let them know you trust them ... have faith in them. Once that has been established, surround those people with time, space and creative freedom, such that they can flourish.

Recalling my first day as editor of *The Yorkshire Post*, Bandeira was sitting in a distant corner of the newsroom, away from the editor's office, doing bits and bobs. Infographics and such. He now sits directly outside my office in the direct line of fire of my whims, leading our editorial line.

I am as proud of this collection of illustrations as Bandeira himself: few journalists – and that is what he is, all 5ft 4in of him – can evoke such poignancy, laughter, loathing and derision in the same way. But that is the raison d'être of the cartoon: to creep where words daren't in order to arouse emotions our prose cannot.

This tome tackles all of life: from terror attacks to sporting heroism; mental health issues to failing Government ministers; and it tackles them with a rare type of dextrous craftsmanship which I am privileged to be able to call upon.

They say a picture speaks a thousand words: Bandeira's articulate far more than that, with an authenticity you can only find in God's Own County.

James Mitchinson
Editor, *The Yorkshire Post*

Back in February 2017, I produced the first cartoon for my regular Saturday slot in *The Yorkshire Post*. It featured Ryan Sidebottom with a paint roller in his hand and white gloss in his hair, in readiness for his retirement and forthcoming DIY duties. It was warmly received. "Honoured, humbled and delighted but I'd appreciate it if you could shave half an inch off my nose..." was his response. I was very encouraged and this sparked the energy to produce week on week something relevant and representative of events. Over one hundred cartoons later and I have managed to compile these into a book which I hope you will find humorous and aesthetically pleasing.

It has always been an ambition to produce a book featuring my work and after consultation with James Mitchinson - editor of *The Yorkshire Post* - it was agreed that if I got 500 retweets then he would sanction permission to proceed. For this I am eternally grateful. I have illustrated for over twenty years at *The Yorkshire Post* and for this book I have applied my skills and quirky sense of humour to produce a collection of cartoons, packed with an eclectic mix of comedy, vibrancy and subtlety, whilst featuring an array of wonderful characters.

Who knows what the next 100 cartoons will bring. Enjoy!

"Honoured, humbled and delighted but I'd appreciate it if you could shave half an inch off my nose… #shirleytemple #leosayer"

Ryan Sidebottom

BANDEIRA...

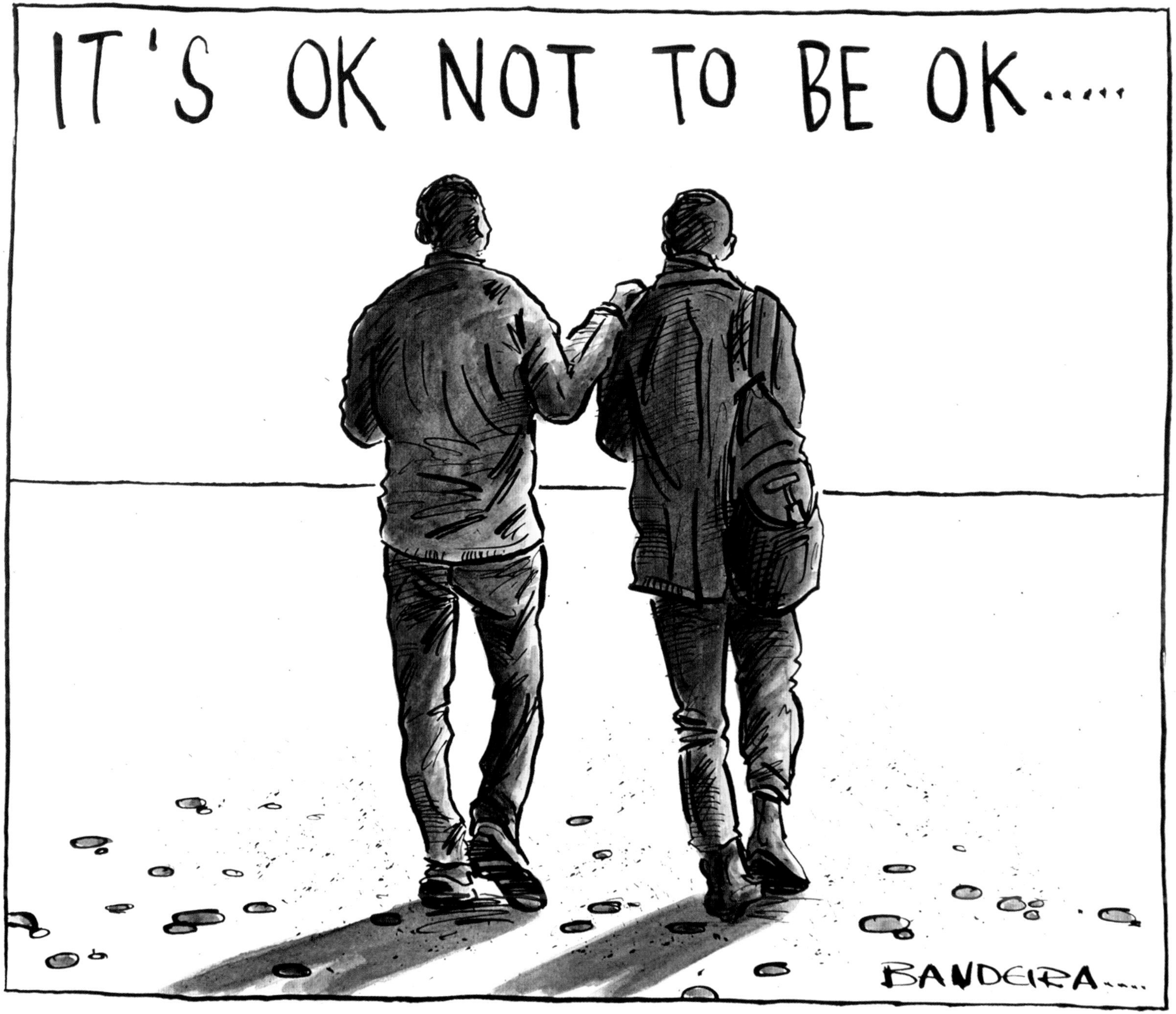
IT'S OK NOT TO BE OK.....
BANDEIRA.....

"I honestly don't know whether to laugh or cry! Though I think it's a marvellous cartoon of me, it's the pigeon that brings the house down"
Henry Blofeld

"It's a fair likeness of me, but you got my dog SPOT ON!"
Julian Norton

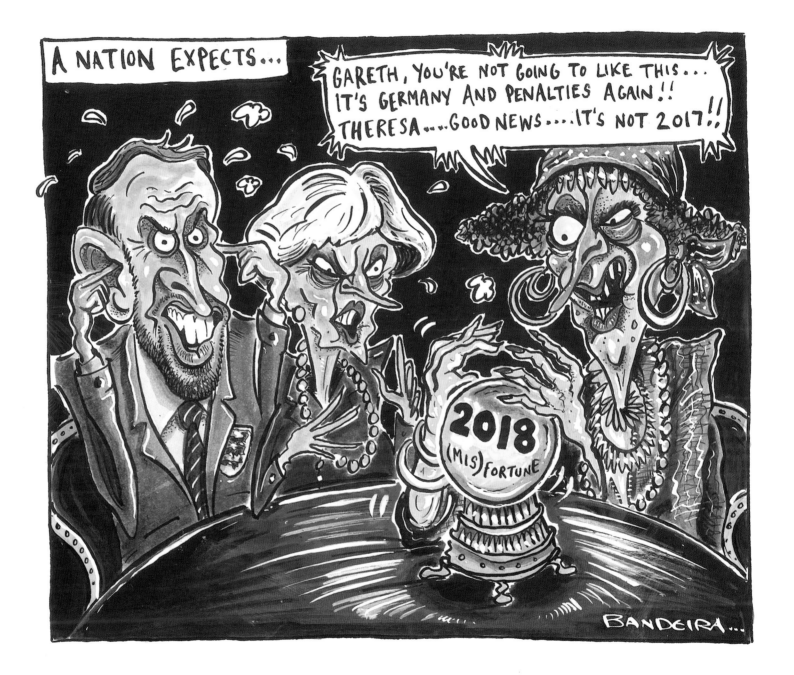

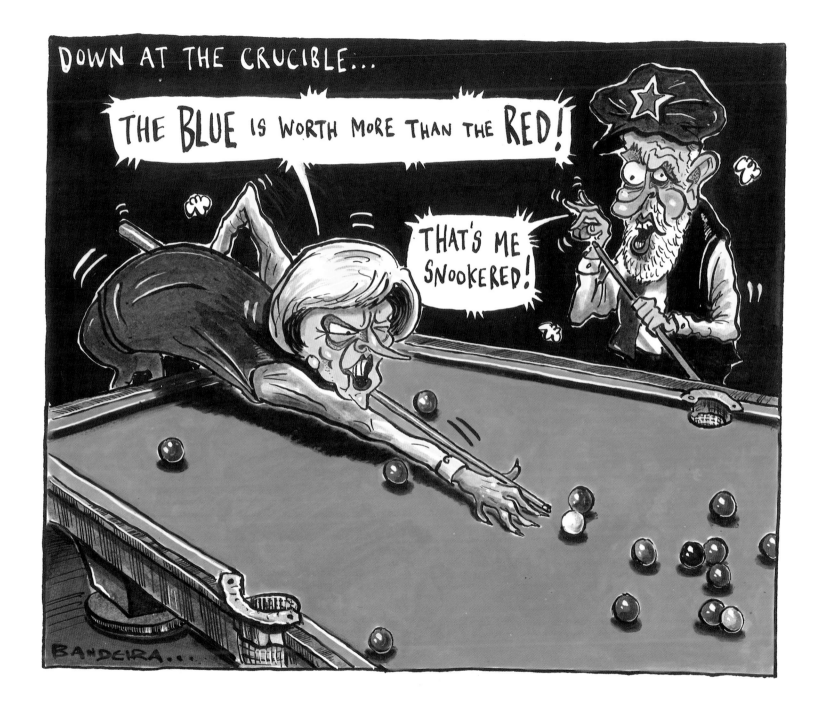

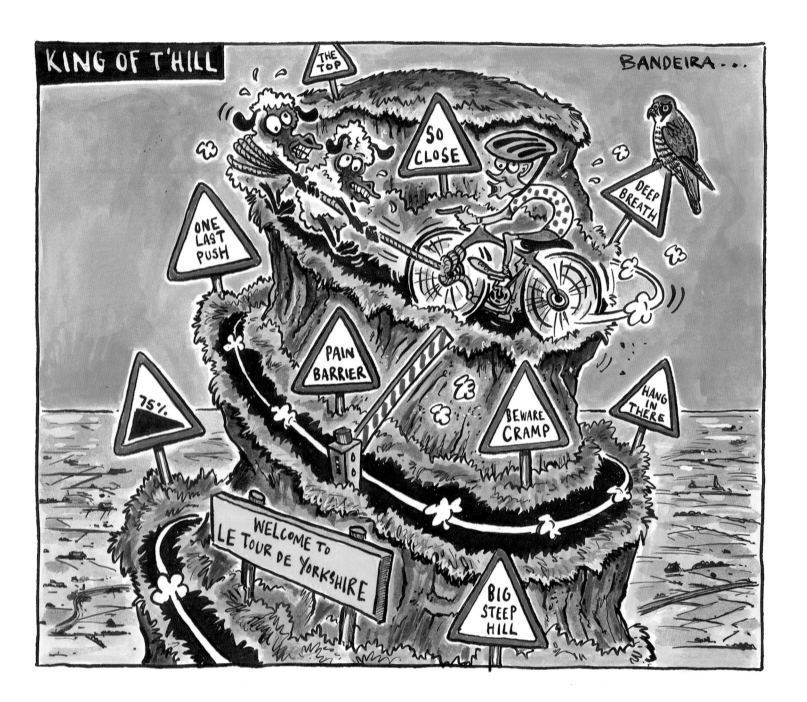

BANDEIRA...

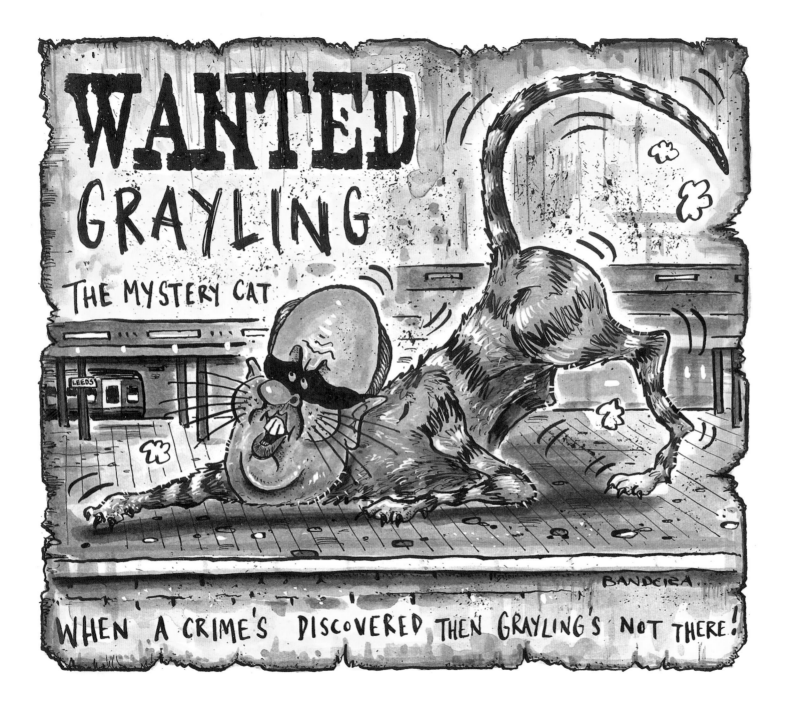

FAILING GRAYLING...
DON'T BLAME ME!
BANDEIRA
Departures
Time Destination Platform Expected
07:50 Ilkley 5b Delayed yet gain
07:56 Skipton 3a Cancelled ag
08:12 Harrogate 1c No driver av labl
08:18 York 2a Broken down
08:27 Dewsbury 15a Cancelled again
08:35 Skipton 3a Get a bus
08:42 Keighley 10a Delayed yet a
08:59 Liverpool 12c Expected 12:
09:12 Hull 16a Walk ther
09:21 Bingley 11b Cancell
09:36 York 2a No cha
09:50 Ilkley 5b Still dela
10:00 Sheffield 13b Tomorro
10:15 Doncaster 13a Don't ask

Recognised as one of Britain's Best Political Cartoons 2018

Quite a lot of my cartoons
have received glowing
tributes and I have been
fortunate to meet
such diverse personalities,
and in some cases
heroes, and challenge
them on their thoughts.
Reaction has always been
positive and that fills me
with great pride.

"Is that for me?
That's spot on
that, lad"
Ricky Tomlinson

"You've made me
better looking"
Peter Beardsley

"I've got a good face for caricature"
Gareth Southgate

"I see you've got my double nose"
George Osborne

"You've got my cheeks spot on"
David Cameron

"You captured my personality of life all in one drawing. I applaud you. Barnsley, beer, cricket and dancing all done with a smile"

Darren Gough

"Graeme studies the individual so that his cartoons and caricatures capture not only the physical likeness of the person but their character, too. There's also a large helping of humour that makes them truly unique"

Ashley Jackson

"Love the ears"
Harry Gration

"I'll sue you for defamation of character"
Dr John Sentamu

BANDEIRA...

"I'll sign the others but not this one. It's great but my husband wouldn't approve"

Theresa May

David W Armitage	Nicholas Carling	Steve Harris	John and Sheila O'Boyle	Rhys Lachlan Sheard
Geoff Askins	Amanda Carter	Patricia Harrison	Ryan Osborne	Stokes Bay 2018
Bill and Jean Bandeira	James Carter	James Hawley	Philip Parkes	Brian John Tempest
Bessie Bandeira	David Carter MBE	Annette Heaton	Jayanti Parmar	John Thompson
Harry Bandeira	Perry Cliff	Andrew P Hicks	Neela Parmar	Peter Thompson
Rachel Baul	Brian Dent	Flynn Hill	Amit Parmar	Hayden Tipling
Mark Bell	Allan and Cynthia Eyre	Megan Hill	Vijal Parmar	Barrie Warner
David Birkinshaw	Eric and Norma Eyre	June Houseman	Andrew Peel	Michael and Joan Watson
Malcolm and Susan Blowers	Tez Exley	Pixie and Stuart Humphries	Mike Porter	Rachel and Garry Wellburn
Terry Bonner	John Feltham	Andy Kingsford	Simon Powell	Peter Westwood
Olga Brand	Andrew Firth	Karen Leaman	Rob Preece	Dawn Whiteley MBE
Keith Bray	Betty Gotts	Michael Lee	Iain Reynolds	Michael R Willoughby
Richard Bray	Margaret and Paul Gotts	David Moreton	Karl Richardson	Andrea Wilson
Stuart Broom	P.R. Gouldsbrough	Alexander and Chris Murray	J. Malcolm Robinson	Sharon Winter
David and Kay Brown	Garry Hale-Newton	Helen Nash	James Robinson	Michael Wood
Michael Carling	Colin Harness	Sandra Joy Newborn	Ian Rogerson	Peter Wood